FOCUS No 11
The decline and present
status of the English lowland
heaths and their vertebrates

COLIN TUBBS

Further copies of this report can be obtained from Interpretative Branch, Nature
Conservancy council, Northminster House, Peterborough, PE1 1UA

ISBN 0-86139-303-1

Contents

SUMMARY

Heathland is a dwarf shrub plant community which in north-west Europe is dominated by heathers and heaths and which arose originally in response to the clearance of the primary woodland. Though anthropogenic in origin it is a habitat which possesses a highly distinctive flora and fauna which today includes many rare or locally distributed species, some of which in Britain are now virtually confined to the remaining heaths.

At the end of the eighteenth century there were at least 190,000ha of heathland in lowland England, distributed mainly on base-deficient soils in the Hampshire and Thames Basins; the Weald; in the south-west peninsular; and in East Anglia. About 25% (48,000ha) survives today. Much of what remains comprises small relicts which are unlikely to support indefinitely many of the animals characteristic of heathland. Much is being invaded rapidly by birch, pine and bracken.

Heathland once occurred widely around the European littoral from Spain to the Baltic. For example, the heaths of Aquitaine in the early nineteenth century were more extensive than those in the whole of lowland England at that time. Yet, from being a common and distinctive element in the landscape and culture of north-west Europe in the first half of the nineteenth century, the heaths there have been reduced to rarity today. The scale on which they have been lost is even greater than in England and in consequence Britain has contracted an international conservation responsibility.

Both in England and continental Europe most heathland has been afforested with conifers or converted to sown leys or even arable. In some districts it has been lost to housing and industry. The chronology of these events varied in detail but the greatest losses have occurred in the twentieth century and the rate of loss has in general accelerated with time.

At least 54% of the heaths in England in varying degrees are protected from physical destruction by their particular ownership or status, though only 13% (6,207ha) are nature reserves or enjoy comparable status. Most heathland in continental Europe survives because it is deliberately protected in some way. In England, none of the protective devices which fall short of nature reserve status is absolutely effective, whilst there are also acute problems of succession from heathland to woodland, notably in the Thames Basin and Weald.

Two species of vertebrates are effectively confined to heathland in Britain (Smooth Snakes and Dartford Warblers). For 7 others, the heaths are especially important because they support a large proportion of the British population. For some, the heaths would seem to be the final refuge in a gradual range retraction to the south and east. Most of these and other vertebrates in heathland are most numerous where the ericaceous vegetation is diversified with scrub, grassland and bog. Size of heathland area and internal habitat variability are important factors in maintaining populations. However, heathland is a rare and fragmented habitat in international terms and it should be seen as important not merely for particular species but for the whole assemblage of inter-related soils, plants and animals which comprise the ecosystem.

INTRODUCTION

Heathland is a dwarf shrub plant community which develops on impoverished, base-deficient soils under comparatively humid conditions and mostly in response to clearance of a primary woodland cover and the associated leaching of nutrients down the soil profile. Such plant communities are rare on the world scale. They are confined mainly to western Europe, southern South Africa, south-east Australia, some oceanic islands and some mountain ranges. In most of western Europe, the plant community is dominated by heather Calluna vulgaris and other ericaceous species and gorse Ulex spp, and extends (or extended) in a discontinuous belt along the seaboard from Spain to the Baltic. Noirfalise and Vanesse (1976) recognised 21 variants of heathland in Europe, of which 9 occur in Britain.

Most of the English lowland heaths belong to the Anglo-Norman type, which is characterised by the presence of bell heather Erica cinerea and dwarf gorse Ulex minor. However, much of the heathland in the south-west peninsular can be assigned to the Armorican type (Erica cinerea, E. ciliaris, U. gallii), whilst some of the coastal heaths there have affinities with Coastal Heaths described from the Basque and Aquitaine coast (the E. vagana heath at the Lizard) and from the Brittany coast (wind-waved Calluna/U. gallii). The heaths have a scattered distribution related primarily to the incidence of base-poor soils developed on sands, gravels and clays overlying geological formations of Mezozoic, Tertiary and Quarternary age. Very extensive heaths formerly occurred in the Hampshire Basin (Dorset and Hampshire); Thames Basin (Hampshire, Berkshire and Surrey); the Weald (Hampshire, Surrey and Sussex); south-west peninsular (Cornwall and Devon); and on the East Anglian coast.

In practice, 'heathland' has been regarded as a mozaic of communities which include acid grassland, valley and seepage step mires and transitional habitats set in a matrix of ericaceous vegetation. All past estimates of the area of heathland in particular areas appear to have included these other communities and for the present purpose I have adopted a similarly wide definition. I include also the grass-heaths of Breckland in East Anglia, though they have a very different geology and land use history to the other heaths. I exclude heaths on the lower ground around the margins of the uplands, for though they are ecologically comparable it seems better to treat them as part of the uplands with which they share a common history of land use and development. The distribution of the lowland heaths dealt with here is shown in Figure 1.

Some heaths in especially exposed positions, notably on the Cornish coast and in the Isles of Scilly, may always have been maintained as heathland by exposure, which limited tree colonisation. However, the evidence suggests that most heathlands in lowland Britain derive from prehistoric clearance of woodland, and have since been maintained by grazing, burning and the removal of invading trees. The heaths must have expanded progressively and were probably at their maximum extent in the sixteenth century, after which they began to decline in area. They have existed long enough to develop a distinctive fauna and flora which includes a few species confined to heathland in Britain, and to sustain peculiar socio-economic systems based on pastoral farming. Most heaths were grazed by cattle and ponies. Some, notably in East Anglia, supported large numbers of sheep. Indeed, the history of Breckland in particular was quite different to that of other areas: clearance began earlier than elsewhere and its later history, from at least the fourteenth century, is dominated by rabbit warrens, sheepwalks and periodic temporary cultivation (Duffey, 1976; Sheail, 1979).

The enclosure and conversion of heathland to more intensive agricultural uses began on a small scale in the sixteenth century. In the eighteenth and nineteenth century most heaths were legally enclosed (though physical enclosure and cultivation did not necessarily follow immediately) and from about 1750 the area of heath began to decline rapidly. Since about 1800, two thirds of the lowland heaths of England have been lost and their associated human pastoral communities have vanished. We must assume that the populations of plants and animals characteristic of heathland have also declined.

This paper compares the past and present extent of the English lowland heaths and assesses the degree to which they currently enjoy protection; considers the significance for some characteristic vertebrates of the heaths which remain; and attempts a prognosis for both heaths and animals.

THE CHRONOLOGY AND EXTENT OF DECLINE

The decline of heathland since about 1800 has been charted for the Hampshire Basin west of the River Avon by Moore (1962), Rippey (1973) and Webb & Haskins (1880); for Breckland by Duffey (1976); and for the Suffolk Sandlings by Chadwick (1982). From maps and other documents I have estimated the former extent of heathland in the Hampshire Basin east of the Avon and in the Weald and Thames Basin. In 1983 I collected information from colleagues about the current extent of lowland heathland and the degree of protection it enjoyed (Table 1). Figure 2 depicts the decline of the heaths in the Hampshire and Thames Basins, western Weald and Sandlings, according to cartographic evidence. There are pitfalls in interpreting this: for example, not all land shown as rough pasture in areas with acid soils is necessarily heathland; where unenclosed woodland and heath occur together (eg the New Forest and Forest of Bere, Hampshire) the former was seldom surveyed accurately and is often arbitrarily shown; and we know from other documents that maps were sometimes wrong. Thus, area measurements derived from maps need cautious treatment and where possible should be checked against other documents. Maps at best provide only a rough estimate. However, the trend is clear and is supported by written sources. In the Hampshire and Thames Basins and in the western Weald there was a steady loss of heathland from c1800 to the later 1920s or early 1930s, after which loss rates accelerated except in the eastern part of the Hampshire Basin. The Sandlings follow a similar trend, though the data do not extend so far back in time. In many areas almost the only heaths left are those which receive some form of protection. So far as can be determined the decline depicted in Figure 2 reflects trends elsewhere, both in lowland Britain and elsewhere in lowland Europe. For example, in Devon the area of lowland rough pasture, including heathland, declined from 58 500ha in 1905 to 19 250ha in 1978 - a 67% loss (Devon County Council and Nature Conservancy Council, 1979).

I estimate from a grid scan of the Old Series Ordnance Survey (mostly published 1810-1820 and surveyed around the turn of the nineteenth century) that there cannot have been less than 190 000ha of heathland in lowland England in c1800. Table 1 records 48,134ha in 1983, which is a 75% loss. For the Hampshire and Thames Basins and western Weald the measurements from the Old Series OS were made with reasonable accuracy and checked against other documents. I estimate that at the end of the eighteenth century there were 97 669ha of heathland in these districts, where there is now at most 32 136ha (1983), representing a 67% loss. About half of what remains is in the New Forest, where heathland declined by only 25% from 21 424ha in c1800 to 16 144ha in 1983.

In fact, there are certainly less than 48,134ha of heathland left in lowland England. No 1983 estimate or measurements were available for the Surrey sectors of the Weald and Thames Basin. The figures for these areas given in Table 1 derive from a 1976 NCC survey and those for Surrey were known at that time to include considerable areas in an advanced stage of succession to woodland, or which were monospecific stands of bracken Pteridium. Successional losses of heathland have undoubtedly increased since 1976.

The decline of heathland in continental Europe was summarised by Noirfalise and Vanesse (1976). The lowland heaths had universally and drastically declined since the nineteenth century. In Aquitaine, almost all of the once vast (200 000ha) heaths had been afforested or (less important) converted to intensive agriculture since 1850. In Brittany, where 20% of the land was heathland in c1850, only 1% remained so. In Belgium and Holland 90% of the heaths had been lost since 1850. In south-west Sweden, where 30% of the land was heath in 1850, only 2% remained so. Almost all the Jutland heaths were destroyed between 1866 and 1955. There and in the Federal Republic of Germany heathland remained only in reserves. A common and distinctive ecosystem had been reduced to rarity in a century or less. Despite the losses sustained in lowland England, the most extensive and intact heaths survive there, and in consequence it can be argued that Britain has contracted an international conservation responsibility in the modern world.

The smaller and more isolated the remaining areas of heath become the less it is likely they they will indefinitely support the full range of associated species. Moore (1962) pointed out in his early study of the Dorset heaths that when a habitat is reduced in size, edge effects become increasingly important and that its key species become increasingly liable to extinction through inbreeding or accident. Bibby & Tubbs (1975) found that the population density of the Dartford Warbler Sylvia undata was related to the size of heathland area: the larger it was the denser the population. Thus, if fragmentation accompanies the total loss of heathland, biological diversity is likely to be further diminished. This has happened to the English lowland heaths and a similar trend is discernable (though there is less data) for those elsewhere in Europe. The trend is illustrated for Dorset in Figure 3 (from Goode, 1981, derived from Moore,1962 and Webb and Haskins, 1980). A similar trend can be discerned elsewhere, except in the New Forest, with the qualification that since 1960 the number of fragments has declined as small, outlying pieces of heath have been converted to farmland, leaving a proportionately larger number of modest sized areas which cannot be encroached upon because they are Ministry of Defence ranges, nature reserves or receive some other protection.

THE CAUSES OF DECLINE

Afforestation and conversion to farmland have been about equally responsible for the loss of heathland in most parts of lowland Britain except Dorset, where Bournemouth arose and grew on heathland. Moore (1962) recorded that 28% of the 1800 heathland in Dorset had been converted to farmland; 20% had been afforested with conifers; and 23% had been taken for urban development. Bournemouth stands on what was once Canford, Poole and Bourne Heaths. In the remainder of the Hampshire Basin and in the Thames Basin and Weald, losses to agriculture predominate, though extensive tracts of former heath have been afforested with conifers. In Breckland, 70% of the heathland losses can be attributed to afforestation (Duffey, 1976); 48% of the Suffolk Sandlings were lost to agriculture and 43% to afforestation between 1930 and 1968 (Chadwick, 1982). The steep declines in the area of heathland which commenced in the 1920s and early 1930s largely reflects the aspirations of the newly formed Forestry Commission. The Commission came close to completely destroying a unique ecosystem in Breckland and did so despite the protests of biologists and an outcry from the public (Sheail, 1979). The large-scale afforestation of heathland in Hampshire and Dorset by the Forestry Commission about the same time raised no comparable protests, but its effects were nearly as profound. In continental Europe, the loss of most of heathland similarly can be attributed about equally to afforestation and conversion to farmland (Noirfalise and Vanesse, 1976).

One line on the graph in Figure 2 is essentially different from the remainder. In the eastern Hampshire Basin most heathland occurs in the New Forest area where the vigorous persistence of a pastoral economy associated with the exercise of common rights over the unenclosed Forest has permitted the survival of most of the heathland. Here a parallel can be drawn with the association of surviving heathland and compatible economic activities in the uplands of both Britain and Europe. In the New Forest large areas were afforested by the former Office of Woods, mainly in the nineteenth century. Public interest in the Forest, an organised body of commoners and protective legislation have prevented further large scale loss, though 810ha of heath were planted with conifers in 1959-61 under a limited provision of the New Forest Act 1947. The unenclosed lands of the Forest, which embrace a mozaic of ancient pasture woodland, heathland, acid and neutral grassland, valley and seepage step mires and the ecotones between them, enjoy protection through the New Forest Acts 1877-1970, which limit the powers of the state to effect changes. The assemblage of habitats comprising the Forest probably represents one of the most important tracts of natural vegetation in Europe.

THE PROTECTION OF SURVIVING HEATHLAND

Of the estimated 48,134 ha of lowland heath which remains, at least 26,000 ha (54%) are protected from afforestation or conversion to agricultural land or physical development because they are nature reserves or enjoy comparable status; are owned by the National Trust or Ministry of Defence; or, in the cases of the New Forest and Ashdown Forest, possess their own protective legislation (Table 1). Probably about 70% of the heaths have also been notified as Sites of Special Scientific Interest under the National Parks & Access to the Countryside Act 1949, and are in the process of being notified under the Wildlife and Countryside Act 1981. The latter Act provides a mechanism whereby owners may be compensated by the NCC for the losses incurred in not maximising the agricultural (or silvicultural) output of their land, though it does not preclude any development for which a local planning authority has given planning permission. The latter in particular might include gravel winning, which has destroyed much heathland in the past, though in general the policies of local authorities embrace the need to protect SSSIs.

Until the Wildlife and Countryside Act 1981 came into operation, it seemed unlikely that most heathland that did not have the benefit of the protective devices and ownerships identified earlier, would survive another decade. This prospect has now receeded, though much will depend on how long government (via the NCC) will be prepared to endure the prospect of financing owners to do nothing with their land.

Besides possible further losses of heathland to agriculture, mineral working and urban or industrial development, many heaths have acute internal management problems. Indeed, the present day total of 48,134 ha is probably a considerable overestimate of the heathland remaining if account were accurately taken of the proportion in a relatively advanced stage of succession to birth, pine or oak woodland, especially in the Thames Basin and Weald. There is need not only to protect the heaths against physical loss but against woodland succession. In many areas the latter battle is being lost or is not being fought.

THE VERTEBRATES OF HEATHLAND

Only two species of vertebrates would seem to be confined to the lowland heaths in Britain - the Dartford Warbler and the Smooth Snake Coronella austriaca. Two further species - the Sand Lizard Lacerta agilis and Natterjack Toad Bufo calamita only also occur in coastal dune systems on the north-west and east coasts. It is hardly surprising that so few vertebrates are confined to heathland if we are correct in assuming the heaths to be of comparatively recent origin, and it is interesting that all four species occur in a wider range of dwarf shrub, scrub and open habitats in more southerly parts of their respective geographical ranges.

A much larger group of vertebrates characteristic of heathland has been recruited from a range of other habitats including the woodland and scrub from which the heathland is assumed to have been derived. This group includes species which are common to other secondary steppe-like habitats such as chalk grassland - notably Skylarks Alauda arvensis, Woodlarks Lullula arborea and Meadow Pipits Anthus pratensis - and species which occur in a variety of scrub and scrub-woodland ecotones, including Nightjars Caprimulgus europaous, Red backed Shrikes Lanius collurio, Stonechats Saxicola torquata, Willow Warblers Phylloscopus trochilis, Grasshopper Warblers Locustella naevia, Whitethroats Sylvia communis, Linnets Acanthis cannabina, Yellow hammers Emberiza citrinella, and Tree Pipits Anthus trivialis. Some heaths, notably in the New Forest where they are drained by numerous valley mires, also support populations of waders (Charadriiformes) - Redshank Tringa totanus, Lapwing Vanellus vanellus, Snipe Gallinago gallinago and Curlew Numenius arquata. The East Anglian heaths have important Stone Curlew Burhinus oedicnemus populations. Heathlands share comparatively few species with the deciduous woodland from which they were ultimately derived, though exceptions are the Adder Vipera berus, Chaffinch Fringilla coelabs and Wren Troglodytes troglodytes. The diversity of the heathland bird community depends mainly on the extent to which the dwarf shrub vegetation is itself diversified by the occurence of patches of gorse, hawthorn, birch or other invasive vegetation. The bird community of continuous tracts of heather is poor both in diversity and density, though it is not similarly impoverished of reptiles: all six species occur on the lowland heaths and can achieve high densities in areas of mature heather diversified only by patches of open sand or bare ground, a habitat which is believed to support large populations of the invertebrates on which they feed.

Lowland heaths are hunting grounds for Buzzards Buteo buteo, Kestrels Falco tinnumculus, Foxes Vulpes vulpes, Stoats Mustula erminea, Weazels Minivalis, Hobbys Falco subbuteo, and in winter, Merlins Falco columbarius, Hen Harriers Circus cyaneus and Great Grey Shrikes Lanius excbitor. However, there is evidence that some heaths are poor feeding grounds because small rodents are few or absent. Probably because of this for example, the density of Foxes is low in the New Forest and Stoats and Weazels are absent. Merlins, Hen Harriers and Great Grey Shrikes are hunters of avian rather than mammalian prey on heathland and Hobbys mainly hunt flying insects over them. The Hobby, is inextricably associated with the lowland heaths and chalk grasslands of Dorset, Hampshire, Wiltshire, Sussex and Surrey and heathland districts there are known to support relatively high breeding densities.

For nine species of vertebrates the heaths are especially important because a large proportion of the British population occurs there. Roughly in order of increasing dependence on heathland they are the Stonechat, Hobby, Nightjar, Woodlark, Red-backed Shrike, Natterjack Toad, Sand Lizard, Smooth Snake and Dartford Warbler. Each is considered briefly below.

Stonechat Saxicola torquata

Magee (1965) reviewed the past status of the Stonechat and concluded that though the species was subject to considerable fluctuations caused by periodic severe winters, there had also been a steady decline in numbers in some areas this century which could not be attributed to cold winters alone, and which was probably due to habitat destruction. His survey yielded information about the numbers breeding in 1961 but it was clearly too incomplete to confidently suggest a total British population. However, it was clear that most Stonechats bred down the western coastal fringe and on the lowland heaths.

Parslow (1973) guessed the British population at 1-10 000 pairs and Sharrock (1976) at 30-60 000 pairs. However, in a survey of the whole of Wales in 1968 (after a period of recovery from cold winters) only 418 breeding pairs plus 89 birds/pairs seen but not proved breeding, could be found (Gibbs and Wood, 1974); a survey of Dartmoor in 1979 revealed a maximum of 137 pairs (Mudge etal, 1981); a survey of Exmoor in 1978 revealed 150 pairs (R.S.P.B., 1978); my own data for the New Forest suggests that the population there can build up to 350 pairs or more between cold winters; and recent data for a large part of the Thames Basin heaths suggest somewhat in excess of 100 pairs there in favourable years (Hants/Surrey Border Bird Reports). From such data it is possible to suggest that the British population in good years is now likely to lie somewhere near the middle of Parslow's order of magnitude, and that around 20% breed on the lowland heaths, excluding those of East Anglia, which possess few Stonechats.

Hobby Falco subbuteo

Parslow (1973) estimated the British population, which is confined to the lowlands, at 85-100 pairs and Sharrock (1976) estimated around 100 pairs. Recent (unpublished) work by a number of biologists strongly suggests more than 300 pairs, spread over heathland, downland and agricultural clayland in southern England. The proportion of this population breeding on or adjoining heathland is probably less than 30% but the population density in heathland districts is high compared with other environments. Recent work (Parr, unpublished) shows that although heathland Hobbys depend extensively on non-heathland birds (notably hirundines and Swifts) which may be caught beyond the confines of the heaths, the large day-flying heathland moths (notably the Emperor Moth Saturnia pavonia and Fox Moth Macrothylacia rubi), dragonflies and other heathland invertebrates are also important food sources which do not occur in more intensively cultivated districts.

Nightjar Caprimulgus europaeus

The Nightjar has declined in numbers and retreated southward and eastweard in Britain since the late 19th century. The rate of both decline and retreat appears to have quickened after about 1930 (Parslow, 1973; Sharrock, 1976; Stafford, 1962; Norris, 1960). Habitat destruction may be a contributory cause but is unlikely to be the ultimate cause. A national BTO survey in 1981 produced 1784 singing males. The main centres of population were (a) the heathlands of Hampshire, Dorset, Surrey, and Sussex and (b) felled conifer woodland in Breckland. The heathland counties of Hampshire, Dorset, Surrey and Sussex, Norfolk and Suffolk, held 1127 (63%) of the total recorded. In most of these counties the species was thought to have been under-recorded in comparison with other areas. Probably 50% of the remaining British population of Nightjars occurs on heathland (Gribble, 1983).

Woodlark Lullula arborea

The Woodlark has withdrawn southwards in Britain since the 19th century, from a distribution which apparently once included most of England and Wales. The population history of the species is complicated by large fluctuations which do not necessarily relate to cold winters. Parslow (1973) described a gradual increase in many counties and especially in south-east England, from about 1920 to 1951, and this despite the severe winters of the 1940s. After 1954 a decline occurred which accelerated after 1960, the severe winters of 1961-2 and 1962-3 causing the virtual collapse of the population. Only about 100 occupied territories were known in 1965, though this is doubtless an underestimate of the total population. Sharrock (1976) suggested a population of 200-450 pairs during 1968-1972. Since at least the early 1960s most of the relict population has occurred on the lowland heaths, mainly in Devon, Cornwall, Dorset, Hampshire, Surrey, Breckland and the Suffolk Sandlings. A survey in Hampshire in 1981 yielded 116 pairs, though the New Forest was inadequately covered, of which all but 11 were on the heaths. A further 104 pairs were found on the heaths of south-west Surrey in 1981. I suggest that the total British population may then have been no more than twice the total of 220 pairs, almost all of which was on heathland. So far as can be determined it has since declined again: the south-west Surrey population was certainly less than 50 pairs in 1982 (local Bird Reports, unpublished data and J. Clark, pers. comm.). There is, however, some indication of an increase in recent years on the Sandlings and Brecks -notably in newly felled plantations rather than pristine heath (D R Langslow).

Red-backed Shrike Lanius collurio

In the 19th century the breeding range included most of England and Wales and the breeding habitat included a wide range of scrub habitats, including hedgerows. In this century the range has retracted south and east and the residual population has been virtually confined to the lowland heaths since the early 1960s. A survey in 1960 gave 253 pairs, with the main concentrations in the New Forest (61) and the Brecks and East Anglian coastal heaths (90). The population subsequently declined to 81 pairs in 1971 (9 in the New Forest; 59 in East Anglia); 44 in 1979; 26-36 in 1980; and 10-15, all in East Anglia, in 1983 (Bibby, 1973; R F Porter pers. comm.).

Natterjack Toad Bufo calamita

The Natterjack has suffered a drastic decline in Britain since about 1940. It formerly occurred on the lowland heaths from Dorset to Norfolk, and in dune habitats on both the east and west coasts. The dune populations have fared rather better than those on the heaths but are nonetheless greatly diminished (Beebee, 1976). On heathland the species is now effectively confined to one area of the Weald. In 1980, the adult Toad population in Britain was thought to be in the region of 20,000 individuals, of which less than 1% remained on heathland (N.C.C., 1983). Beebee (1977) suggested that the decline of the heathland populations has been associated with a combination of changes in habitat (mainly the invasion of pine, birch, gorse and bracken) and the fragmentation of the heaths themselves, but this explanation does not seem entirely satisfactory for there remain large areas of apparently suitable heathland habitat, many of which formerly held Natterjacks.

Sand Lizard Lacerta agilis

The Sand Lizard's distribution in Britain closely follows that of the heaths of the Hampshire and Thames Basins and Western Weald, with a relict outlier on coastal dunes in Merseyside (N.C.C., 1983). Of an estimated population of 7-8,000 in 1976, all but c.200 were on the heaths. The species has been greatly reduced and fragmented in distribution since at least the late 1930s, apparently through a combination of habitat fragmentation and the increasing susceptibility of the remaining heaths to adverse internal changes in lizard habitat. Corbett and Tamarind (1979) described Sand Lizards as being confined to mature dry heath (Calluna-Erica cinerea-Ulex minor). Tree invasion of many heaths in the Thames Basin combined with excessive burning there and elsewhere are suggested as the main causes of decline. The remaining colonies are isolated and with isolation comes greater vulnerability to extinction.

Smooth Snake Coronella austriaca

So far as we know the Smooth Snake has always been confined to the lowland heaths of the Hampshire Basin, Thames Basin and extreme western Weald in Britain, though there are old records from outlying areas which may or may not be authentic. The species' habitat preference appears to be similar to that of the Sand Lizard but it also persists at low densities in a wider variety of heathland habitats. The total population may be of the order of 2,000 individuals (N.C.C., 1983). However, like the Sand Lizard, its distribution has become fragmented as excessive burning on the one hand and tree colonisation on the other have changed much of what remains. Like the Sand Lizard it is a rare animal in Britain, and it is dependent on what remains of the lowland heaths for its survival here.

Dartford Warbler Sylvia undata

The Dartford Warbler is a bird of maritime western Europe and reaches the northern limit of its range in southern England. It may always have been confined there to the lowland heaths and though it was once more widespread it has been confined since the 1940s to the heaths of the Hampshire and Thames Basins, with small populations becoming established elsewhere from time to time. It is highly vulnerable to severe winter weather and populations have consequently fluctuated widely. After the 1962-63 winter there may have been as few as 11 pairs left, whereas a survey in 1974 gave about 560 pairs, of which 286 were on the Dorset heaths and 250 on those of the New Forest, (Bibby and Tubbs, 1975). It has since declined and then increased again, with large scale recolonisation of the Thames Basin heaths. The population may now lie somewhere in the region of 5-600 pairs.

There is little precise information about the numbers and distribution of Dartford Warblers in Britain before 1960, but from the literature it is clear that they were formerly permanently established over a wider area. For the main centres of their present distribution in the Hampshire and Thames Basins and western Weald, extrapolation suggests 1 000 pairs in about 1930 and 1 600 pairs in about 1800, assuming the heathland which has been lost held similar densities to that which remains. The population is likely to have been much larger, because, first, we know that large areas of heath support higher densities than small areas and there were once more of the former, and, second, a larger and more widespread population may have have been better buffered against depletion by severe weather than recently. Habitat loss would appear to have compounded vulnerability to severe winters to leave the species in a tenuous position in Britain.

Of the nine species, only the Hobby is not known to have declined. At least two (Red-backed Shrike and Nightjar) belong to a group of insectivorous migratory birds whose range has contracted to the south and east in Britain during this century, whilst some, including the Red-backed Shrike, are declining elsewhere in north-west Europe. Though habitat destruction may be a contributory factor in the declines, it is clearly not the ultimate cause, which may be linked with changing climate (cooler, wetter springs) and food supply or with more subtle factors of which we remain unaware. At least two other species (Dartford Warbler and Stonechat) and perhaps a third (Woodlark) have probably been most influenced by the reduction of suitable habitat. In the case of the Woodlark this may not be merely a loss of heathland and other steppe like habitats: variations in the amounts of short vegetation in which to feed are also important, and this depends (on heathland) on the incidence of fire in suitable places. The species was probably one of a very few to benefit from the otherwise disasterous heath fires of the exceptionally dry summer of 1976.

Four of the six species of birds (the Shrike, Nightjar, Woodlark and Stonechat) have tended to retreat to heathland in south-east England as their range has contracted and their populations have diminished. This may conceivably be true of a fifth, the Dartford Warbler. However, the Dartford Warbler and the three herptiles can best be seen as comprising a group which appears to be adapted to and historically to have been limited to heathland. Their population declines are most likely to be directly related to the decline in the amount of suitable heathland habitat.

Of the nine birds and three herptiles, eight are wholly or mainly insectivorous. One (the Hobby) is partly so. None of the birds are characteristic of uniform ericaceous heathland. All are ecotone species which occur where Calluna/Erica is diversified by gorse, invading trees, or by wet valleys, situations in which invertebrate prey appears especially abundant when compared with other open habitats in the lowlands, most of which in any case appear to have suffered even higher loss rates than the heaths. Heathland may simply be the most viable remaining habitat for insectivorous species whose decline through climatic change acting on food supply is compounded by the physical destruction of habitat. The herptiles are clearly more closely adapted to heathland and I speculate that this specialisation arises from a balance between their thermo-regulatory needs (which would not be satisfied in denser cover) and the protection from predators provided by deep heather.

In sum, the lowland heaths have increased in relative importance as the final refuge in Britain for a number of rare vertebrates which have declined in numbers and retracted in range during this century. It would be wrong, however, to see the heaths only in terms of their capacity to sustain these species. It is better to regard the nine species as standing proxy for the whole, peculiar, heathland, ecosystem, which demands conservation not for any one of its component parts but for the assemblage of interelated soils, plants and animals of which it is comprised (Farrell, 1983).

CONCLUSIONS

THE SURVIVING HEATHLAND

A reasonable prognosis for the conservation of the remaining heathland in lowland England would appear to be:-

1. In the short term, protective tenures and SSSI status will protect most remaining heathland.

2. Where it is protected only by SSSI status the long term future of heathland will depend on the willingness of government to finance compensatory agreements.

3. Heathland unprotected by these devices is likely to be lost.

4. The future of the heathland which is Ministry of Defence property is secure only so long as the holdings are not disposed of, they are not excessively damaged by tracked vehicles, and individual managers are well-disposed to conservation.

5. Large areas of heathland will be irretrievably lost to woodland, unless tree clearance is undertaken on a large scale in the Thames Basin and Weald.

HEATHLAND VERTEBRATES

I draw the following conclusions about the future of the nine species to which I have particularly alluded:-

1. The Red-backed Shrike will be lost as a heathland breeding species in the immediate future ; and the Nightjar may ultimately follow unless there is a sustained shift towards warmer, drier springs, There are no conservation prescriptions which might prevent the loss of either species, though it is possible that Nightjar populations might be locally and temporarily boosted by increasing the amount of wood-heath ecotones in suitable localities, as has been done successfully by the RSPB at Minsmere.

2. The survival in Britain of the Woodlark and Dartford Warbler will probably depend on the maintenance of at least the order of the present area of heathland within their respective breeding ranges, to permit sufficient population growth during favourable periods to overcome the setbacks of periodic severe winters. Bibby (1978) has suggested ways of managing heathland for Dartford Warblers and it would not be impossible also to create a patchwork of suitable areas for Woodlarks on many heaths. Positive management would help to sustain both species.

3. The populations of the three herptiles are now so fragmented that their ultimate survival on heathland probably depends not only on protection of the habitat against development but its positive management. The Smooth Snake is in the least precarious position.

4. The national populations of the Stonechat and Hobby would be significantly reduced were there to be further large scale losses of heathland, but neither would be lost as a British breeding species.

ACKNOWLEDGEMENTS

I wish to thank the following colleagues who provided information about the present extent and protection of heathland and answered a multiplicity of questions:
M J D'Oyley; C F Durrell; R D M Edgar; C L A Fry; C J Hadley; D H Harvey; J F Lamerton; G P Radley; P Sargeant; C J D Shackles; P C Tinning; J R White; P A Wright.
I am also grateful to D R Langslow, A S Cooke, A E Stubbs and Miss L Farrell for commenting on a draft.

REFERENCES

Beebee, T J C. 1976. The Natterjack Toad (Bufo calamita) in the British Isles: a study of past and present status. Brit. J. Herpetology, **5**, 515-521.

Beebee, T J C. 1977. Environmental changes as a cause of Natterjack Toad (Bufo calamita) declines in Britain. Biol. Conserv., **11**, 87-102.

Bibby, C J & Tubbs, C R. 1975. Status, habits and conservation of the Dartford Warbler in Britain. Brit. Birds, **68**, 177-195.

Bibby, C J. 1978. Conservation of the Dartford Warbler on English lowland heaths: a review, Biol. Conserv., **13**, 299-307.

Chadwick, L. 1982. In Search of Heathland, Dennis Dobson, London.

Corbett, K F & Tamarind, D L. 1979. Conservation of the Sand Lizard Lacerta agilis, by habitat management, Brit. J. Herpetology, **5**, 799-823.

Devon County Council and Nature Conservancy Council, 1979. The Changing Face of Devon.

Dufey, E. 1976. Breckland. in: Nature in Norfolk, Jarrold, Norwich.

Farrell, L. 1983. Heathland Management, Focus on Nature Conservation No 2., Nature Conservancy Council.

Gibbs, R G and Wood, J B. 1974. A 1968 survey of the status of the Stonechat in Wales, Nature in Wales, **14**, 7-12.

Goode, D. 1981. The threat to wildlife habitats, New Scientist, 22 January 1981, 219-223.

Gribble, F. 1983. Nightjars in Britain and Ireland in 1981. Bird Study, **30**, 165-176.

Magee, J D. 1965. The breeding distribution of the Stonechat in Britain and the causes of its decline, Bird Study, **12**, 83-89.

Moore, N W. 1962. The heaths of Dorset and their conservation, J. Ecol., **50**, 369-391.

Mudge, G P, Davies, M, Crooke, C H, Booth, R G and Smith, S E A. 1981. Breeding bird populations of the open moorland of Dartmoor in 1979, Devon Birds, **34**, 28-46.

Nature Conservancy Council, 1983. The Ecology and Conservation of Amphibian and Reptile Species Endangered in Britain.

Noirfalise, A & Vanesse R. 1976. Heathlands of Western Europe. Council of Europe European Committee for the Conservation of Nature and Natural Resources.

Norris, C A. 1960. The breeding distribution of thirty bird species in 1952, Bird Study, **7**, 129-184.

Parslow, J. 1973. Breeding Birds of Britain and Ireland: A Historical Review, Poyser, Berkhamsted.

Rippey, B H R T. 1973. The Conservation of the Dorset Heaths - a factual study. M.Sc.thesis, University College, University of London.

Royal Society for the Protection of Birds, 1978. Exmoor Moorland Ornithological Survey 1978. Unpub. report.

Sharrock, J T R(ed.). 1976. The Atlas of Breeding Birds in Britain and Ireland. British Trust for Ornithology.

Sheail, J. 1979. Documentary evidence of the changes in the use, management and appreciation of the grass-heaths of Breckland. J. Biogeog., 6, 277-292.

Stafford, J. 1962. Nightjar Inquiry, 1957-58, Bird Study, 9, 104-115.

Webb, N R & Haskins, L E. 1980. An ecological study of heathlands in the Poole Basin, Dorset, England, Biol. Conserv., 17, 281-296.

ENGLISH LOWLAND HEATHLAND AND ITS PROTECTION IN 1983

TABLE 1

Underlined figures are from a 1976 NCC survey: no subsequent data were available. 'Special statutory protection' refers to the protection conferred on the New Forest and Ashdown Forest by special Acts of Parliament peculiar to those areas.

Area	Total Heath (ha)	SSSI	Nature Res or similar protection	National Trust (1)	Ministry of Defence	Special statutory protection	Total protected (ha) (2)
Hampshire Basin (East of R Avon)	16,348	15,827	20	828	50	14,427	15,325
Hampshire Basin (West of R Avon)	5,670	3,175	1,637		700		2,337
Weald (Hampshire)	1,600	1,292	38	385	1,183		1,606
Weald (W Sussex)	1,669	362	89	239			328
Weald (Surrey)	2,127	No data (6)	569	No data (5)	No data		569
Weald (E Sussex)	600	600				509	509
Thames Basin (Hampshire)	948	594	289		468		757
Thames Basin (Surrey)	3,774	No data (6)	No data	No data	No data (3)		
Thames Basin (Berkshire)	160	160	32				32
Devon	2,000	1,100	180				180
Cornwall & Scillies	4,600 (4)	2,000	665	No data	No data		665

Area	Total Heath (ha)	SSSI	Nature Res or similar protection	National Trust (1)	Ministry of Defence	Special statutory protection	Total protected (ha) (2)
Breckland	4,542	3,668	671		1,076		1,747
Suffolk Sandlings	1,580	830	405	92			497
North Norfolk	729	453	57				57
West Midlands	1,685	1,659	1,500	20			1,520
Lincolnshire	102	102	55				55
TOTALS	**48,134**	**31,822**	**6,207**	**1,564**	**3,477**	**14,936**	**26,184**

Notes:-

(1) The areas given in this column exclude National Trust lands which are also nature reserves.

(2) The areas shown in this column are the sum of those in the preceeding four columns.

(3) Though no figure is available, it is known that most of the heathland in the Thames Basin in Surrey is owned by the Ministry of Defence.

(4) Provisional figures: definitive data derived from detailed survey in 1983-4 is awaited.

(5) It is known that a substantial area of the remaining heathland is owned by the National Trust.

(6) Though the area of SSSIs containing heathland is known, the considerable proportion which has succeeded to woodland has not been measured.

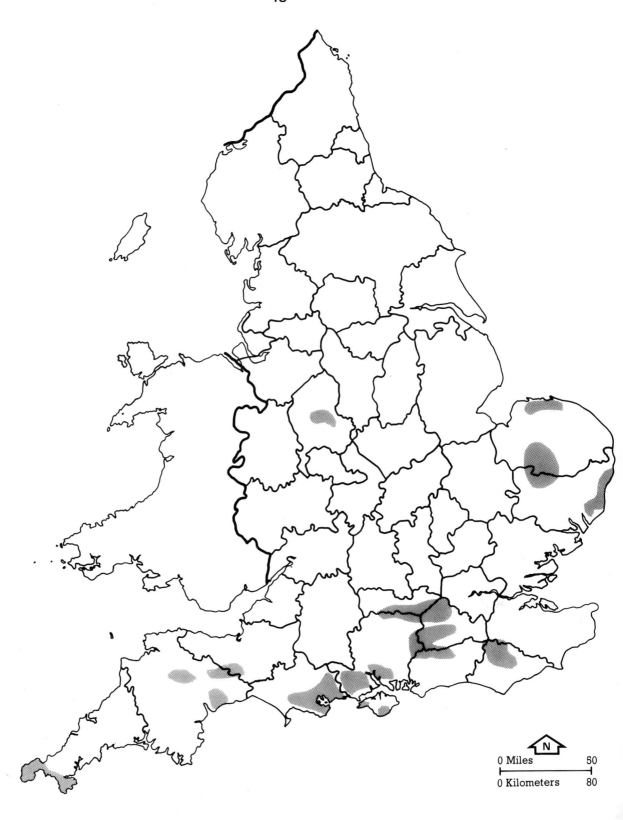

FIGURE 1: MAIN AREAS OF LOWLAND HEATH IN ENGLAND

19

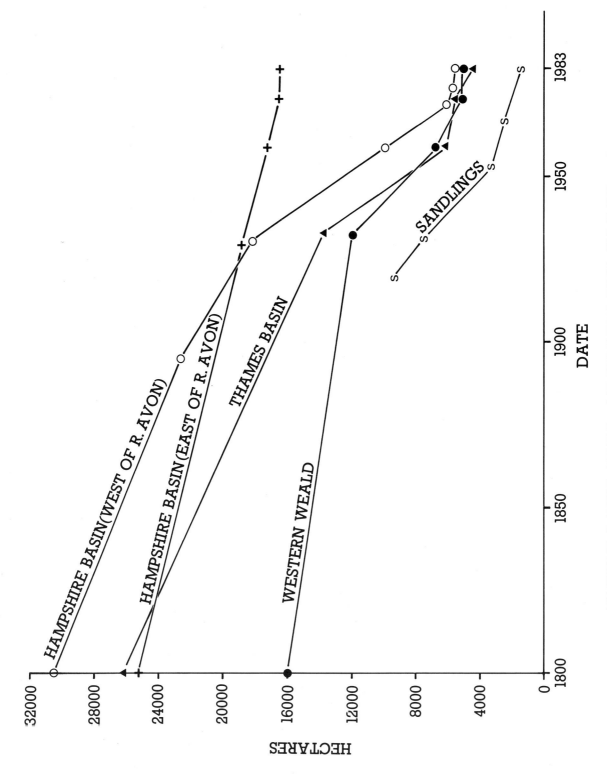

FIGURE 2: THE AREA OF HEATHLAND IN DIFFERENT
GEOGRAPHICAL AREAS IN LOWLAND ENGLAND, 1800-1983

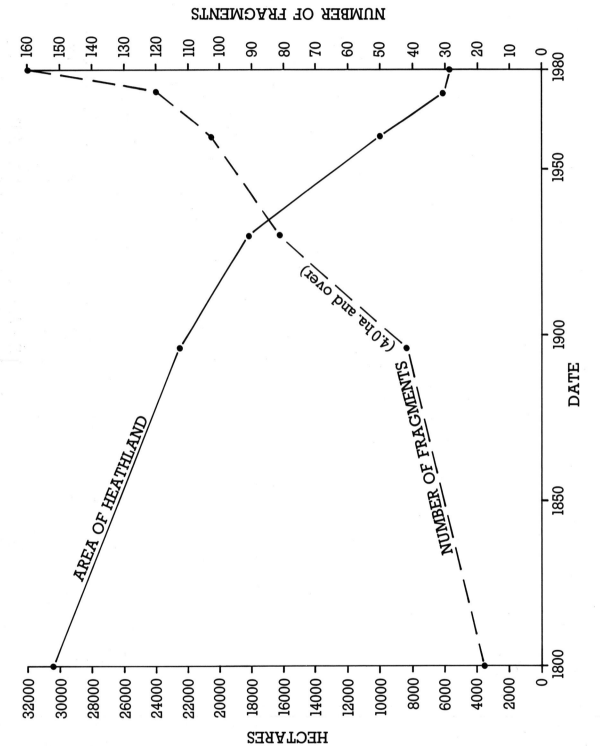

FIGURE 3: THE AREA OF HEATHLAND AND NUMBER OF FRAGMENTS OF 4.0 HECTARES AND OVER IN THE HAMPSHIRE BASIN WEST OF THE RIVER AVON, 1800-1980. [From Goode (1981) derived from Moore (1962) and Webb and Haskins (1980).]